Arranged for *all* electronic keyboards *by Ke*

THE COMPL
KEYBOARD PLAYER
Bee Gees

Wise Publications
London / New York / Paris / Sydney / Copenhagen / Berlin / Madrid / Tokyo

Exclusive Distributors:
Music Sales Limited
8/9 Frith Street, London W1V 5TZ, England.
Music Sales Pty Limited
120 Rothschild Avenue, Rosebery, NSW 2018, Australia.

This book © Copyright 1990, 2002 by
Wise Publications.
Order No. AM78668
ISBN 0-7119-2150-4

Compiled by Peter Evans.
Music arranged by Kenneth Baker.
Music processed by Music Print.
Cover photograph courtesy of Corbis Images.
Printed in the United Kingdom by
Caligraving Limited, Thetford, Norfolk.

Your Guarantee of Quality
As publishers, we strive to produce every book
to the highest commercial standards.
This book has been carefully designed to minimise awkward
page turns and to make playing from it a real pleasure.
Particular care has been given to specifying acid-free, neutral-sized paper
made from pulps which have not been elemental chlorine bleached.
This pulp is from farmed sustainable forests and was produced with special
regard for the environment. Throughout, the printing and binding have been
planned to ensure a sturdy, attractive publication which should give years of enjoyment.
If your copy fails to meet our high standards, please inform us and
we will gladly replace it.

www.musicsales.com

MASSACHUSETTS

Words & Music by Barry Gibb, Robin Gibb & Maurice Gibb

Suggested registration: clarinet
Rhythm: rock
Tempo: medium (♩ = 92)

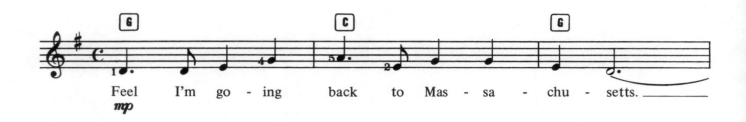

Feel I'm go - ing back to Mas - sa - chu - setts. _____

mp

_____ Some - thing's tell - ing me I must go

home. _____ And the lights all went

cresc.

out in Mas - sa - chu - setts, the day I

mf   *dim.*

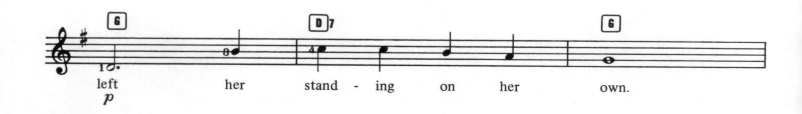

left her stand - ing on her own.

p

clarinet to hawaiian guitar

Tried to hitch a ride to San Fran -
mp

cis - co. _____ Got - ta do the

things I wan - na do. _____ And the
cresc.

lights all went out in Mas - sa - chu - setts, they brought me
mf *dim.*

back to see my way with you. They brought me
p *cresc.*

back to see my way with you. stop rhythm
mf

NEW YORK MINING DISASTER 1941

Words & Music by Barry Gibb & Robin Gibb

Suggested registration: piano
Rhythm: rock
Tempo: medium (♩ = 96)

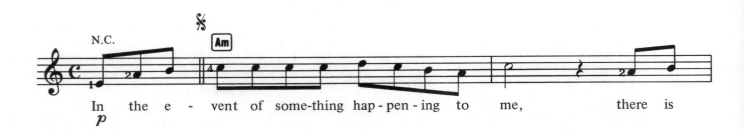

In the e - vent of some-thing hap - pen - ing to me, there is

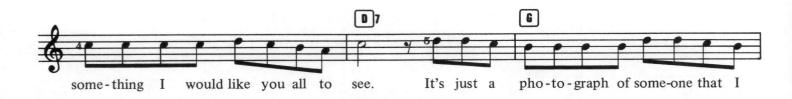

some-thing I would like you all to see. It's just a pho-to-graph of some-one that I

knew. Have you seen my wife, Mis - ter Jones? Do you

know what it's like on the out - side? Don't go talk - ing too loud, you'll cause a

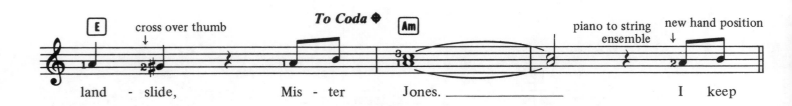

land - slide, Mis - ter Jones. _____ I keep

strain - ing my ears to hear a sound. May - be some - one is dig - ging un - der -

ground. Or have they giv - en up and all gone home to bed, think - ing

those who once ex - ist - ed must be dead? Have you seen my wife, Mis - ter

Jones? Do you know what it's like on the out - side? Don't go

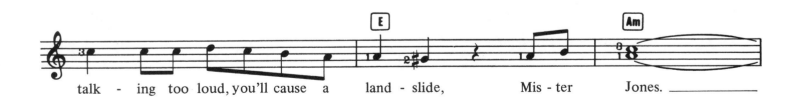

talk - ing too loud, you'll cause a land - slide, Mis - ter Jones. _____

D.%. al Coda   ⊕ *CODA*

_____   In the e -   Jones. _____

N.C.   *rit.*   cross over thumb

stop rhythm

7

WORDS

Words & Music by Barry Gibb, Robin Gibb & Maurice Gibb

Suggested registration: piano
Rhythm: rock
Tempo: fairly slow (♩ = 84)

Smile an ev-er-last-ing smile, a smile could bring you near to me.

change finger

Don't ev-er let me find you gone, 'cause that would bring a

cross over thumb

tear to me. This world has lost its glo-ry,

new hand position

let's start a brand new sto-ry now, my love. Right

now, there'll be no oth-er time, and I can show you how, my

love. _____ Talk in ev - er - last -ing words, and ded - i - cate them

all to me. _____ And I will give you all my

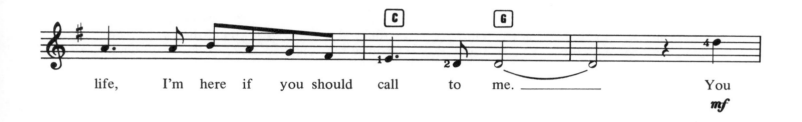
life, I'm here if you should call to me. _____ You

think that I don't ev - en mean a sin - gle word I say.

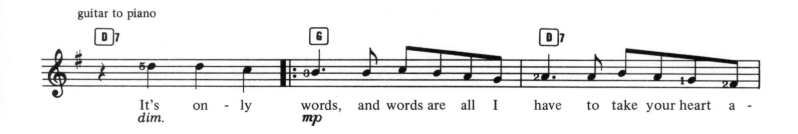
It's on - ly words, and words are all I have to take your heart a -

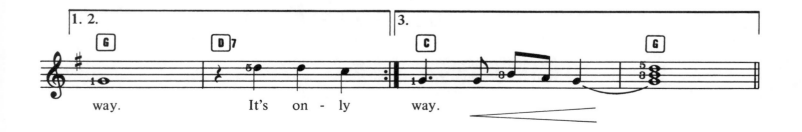
way. It's on - ly way.

HOW DEEP IS YOUR LOVE

Words & Music by Barry Gibb, Robin Gibb & Maurice Gibb

Suggested registration: guitar
Rhythm: rock
Tempo: medium (♩ = 108)

I know your eyes in the morn - ing sun, I feel you touch __
me, I be - lieve in you. You know the door __

__ me in the pour - ing rain. And the mo - ment that you wan - der
__ to my ver - y soul. You're the light __ in my deep - est,

far from me, __ I wan - na feel you in my arms a - gain. __ And you
dark - est hour, __ you're my sav - ior __ when I fall. __ And you

come to me __ on a sum - mer breeze, keep me warm in your love __ then you
may not think __ I care for you, __ when you know down in - side __ that I

soft - ly leave. And it's me you need __ to show: __ How deep is your
real - ly do. __ And it's me you need __ to show: __ How

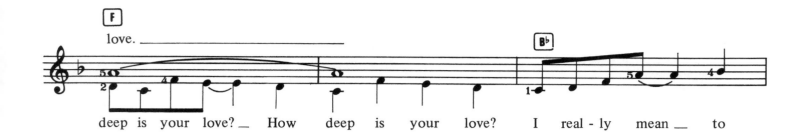

love. _____ deep is your love? _ How deep is your love? I real - ly mean _ to

cross over 5th finger

learn, ___ 'cause we're liv - ing in a world of fools, break - ing us

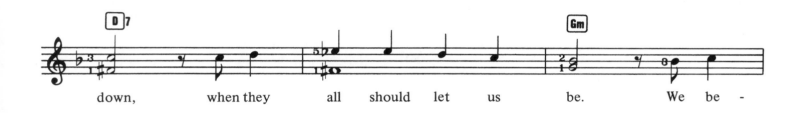

down, when they all should let us be. We be -

long to you and me.
mp

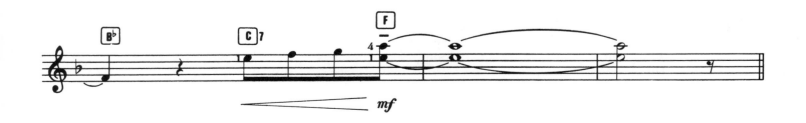

mf

MORE THAN A WOMAN

Words & Music by Barry Gibb, Robin Gibb & Maurice Gibb

Suggested registration: guitar
Rhythm: disco
Tempo: medium (♩ = 108)

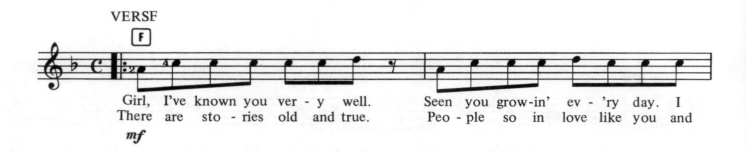

Girl, I've known you ver - y well. Seen you grow-in' ev - 'ry day. I
There are sto - ries old and true. Peo - ple so in love like you and

nev - er real - ly looked be - fore. But now you take my breath a - way.
me, and I can see my - self, let His - to - ry re - peat it - self. Re -

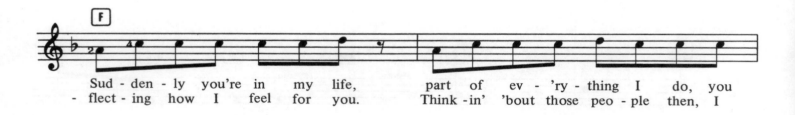

Sud - den - ly you're in my life, part of ev - 'ry - thing I do, you
- flect - ing how I feel for you. Think - in' 'bout those peo - ple then, I

got me work - ing day and night, just tryin' to keep a hold on you.
know that in a thou - sand years I'd fall in love with you a - gain.

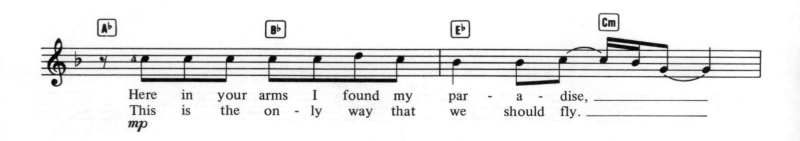

Here in your arms I found my par - a - dise, _____
This is the on - ly way that we should fly. _____

my on-ly chance for hap-pi-ness. _____ And if I lose you now, I
This is the on-ly way to go. _____ And if I lose your love, I

think I would die. _____ ⎫ Oh, say you'll al-ways be my ba-by, we can make it shine. _
know I would die. _____ ⎭
cresc.

add string ensemble

We can take for-ev-er, just a min-ute at a time. _ Oh, _____

CHORUS

More than a wom-an.
f

More than a wom-an to me. _

_____ More than a wom-an. More than a wom-an to me. _

(Repeat first 4 bars of CHORUS and fade for ending)

_____ Oh. _____

WORLD

Words & Music by Barry Gibb, Robin Gibb & Maurice Gibb

Suggested registration: string ensemble. Arpeggio, if available
Rhythm: rock
Tempo: quite slow (♩ = 92)

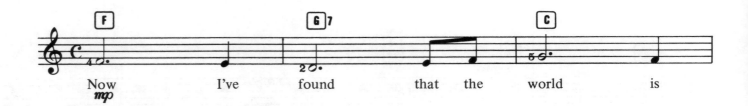

Now I've found that the world is

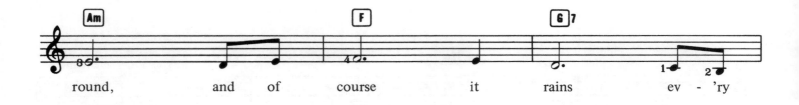

round, and of course it rains ev - 'ry

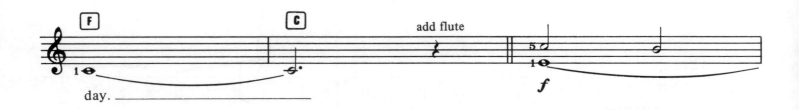

day. _____

Liv - ing to - mor - row, _____ where in the world will I

be? To - mor - row, _____ how far am I a - ble to

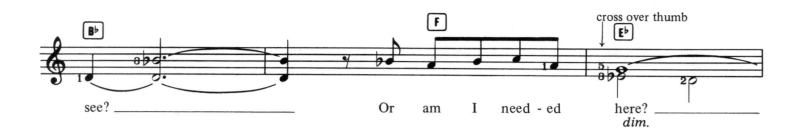

see? _____ Or am I need - ed here? _____
dim.

cross over thumb

Now I've found that the
mp

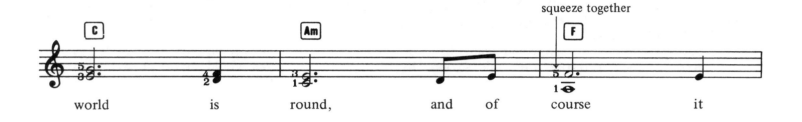

squeeze together

world is round, and of course it

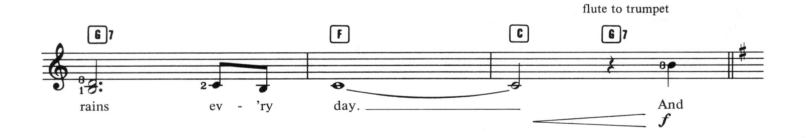

flute to trumpet

rains ev - 'ry day. _____ And
f

now I've found that the world is round, and of

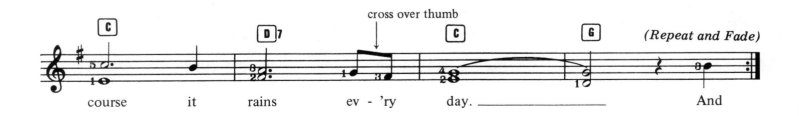

cross over thumb

(Repeat and Fade)

course it rains ev - 'ry day. _____ And

15

HOW CAN YOU MEND A BROKEN HEART

Words & Music by Barry Gibb & Robin Gibb

Suggested registration: saxophone
Rhythm: swing
Tempo: slow (♩ = 76)

VERSE

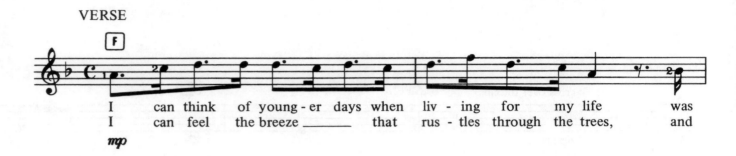

I can think of young-er days when liv-ing for my life was
I can feel the breeze _____ that rus-tles through the trees, and

ev-'ry-thing a man could want to do. I could nev-er see to-
mist-y mem-o-ries of days gone by. We could nev-er see to-

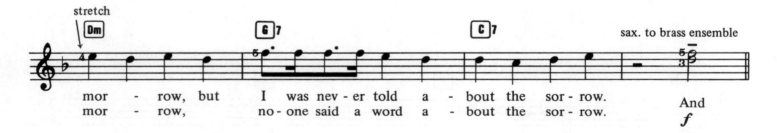

mor-row, but I was nev-er told a-bout the sor-row.
mor-row, no-one said a word a-bout the sor-row. And

CHORUS

how can you mend _____ a bro-ken heart? _____ How can you stop the rain from fall-ing

down? How _____ can you stop the sun from shin-ing? _____

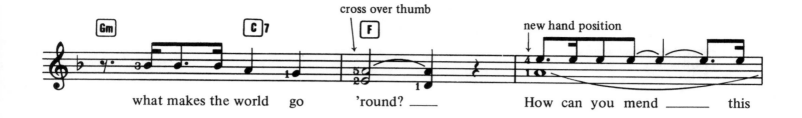

cross over thumb

new hand position

what makes the world go 'round? ___ How can you mend ___ this

new hand position

bro-ken man? ___ How can a los - er ev - er win? Please

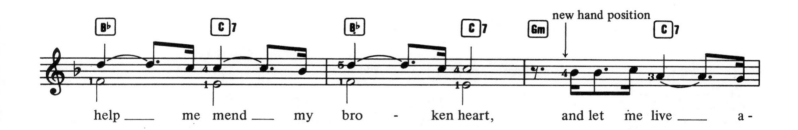

new hand position

help ___ me mend ___ my bro - ken heart, and let me live ___ a-

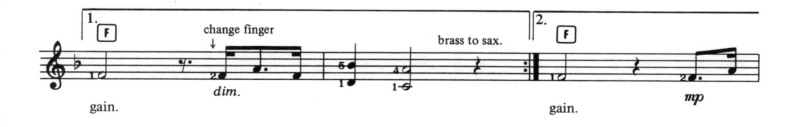

1.

change finger

brass to sax.

2.

gain. dim. gain. mp

ad lib.

stretch   stretch

stop rhythm

I'VE GOT TO GET A MESSAGE TO YOU

Words & Music by Barry Gibb, Robin Gibb & Maurice Gibb

Suggested registration: guitar
Rhythm: rock
Tempo: medium (♩ = 96)

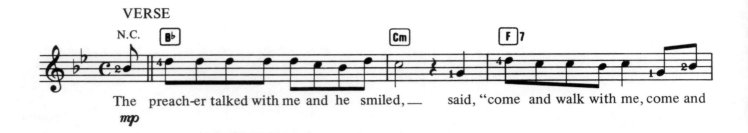

The preach-er talked with me and he smiled, ___ said, "come and walk with me, come and

walk one more mile. ___ Now for once in your life ___ you're a - lone, ___ but you

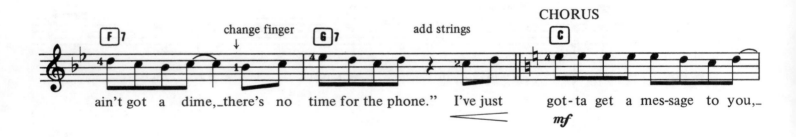

ain't got a dime, ___ there's no time for the phone." I've just got-ta get a mes-sage to you, ___

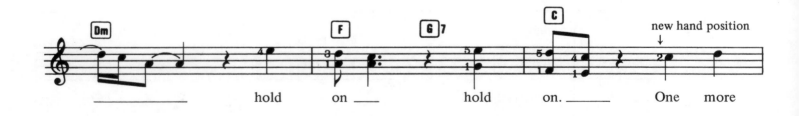

___ hold on ___ hold on. ___ One more

hour, and my life will be through, ___ hold on, ___ hold

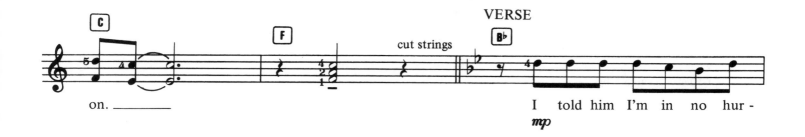

on.

VERSE

I told him I'm in no hur -

ry, but if I broke her heart, then won't you tell her I'm sor - ry, and for

once in my life I'm a - lone, and I got - ta let her know, just in

CHORUS

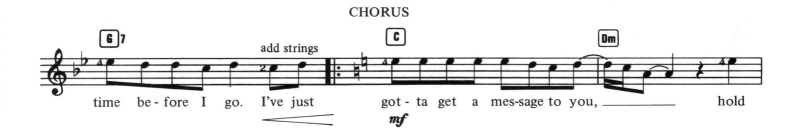

time be - fore I go. I've just got - ta get a mes-sage to you, hold

on, hold on. One more hour and my life will be through,

(Repeat and Fade)

hold on, hold on. I've just

IF I CAN'T HAVE YOU

Words & Music by Barry Gibb, Maurice Gibb & Robin Gibb

Suggested registration: organ (with tremolo)
Rhythm: rock
Tempo: medium (♩ = 108)

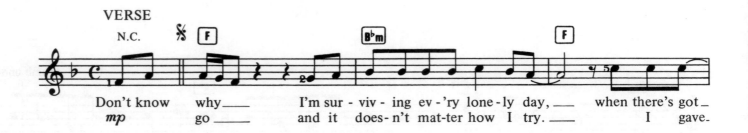

VERSE

Don't know why___ I'm sur - viv - ing ev - 'ry lone - ly day, ___ when there's got___
go ___ and it does - n't mat - ter how I try. ___ I gave___

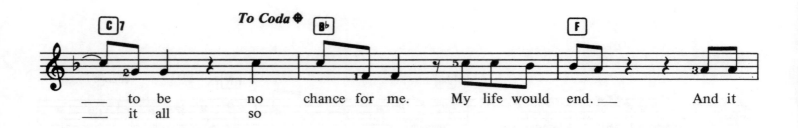

To Coda

___ to be no chance for me. My life would end. ___ And it
___ it all so

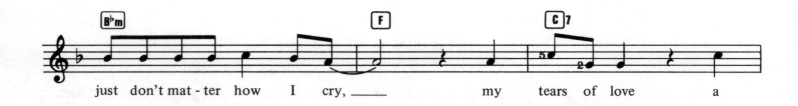

just don't mat - ter how I cry, ___ my tears of love a

waste of time. If I turn a - way, am I strong e - nough to see it

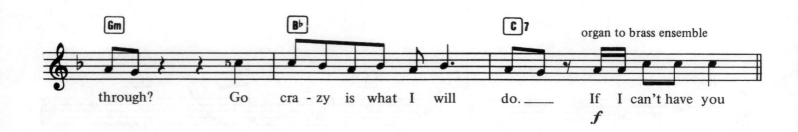

organ to brass ensemble

through? Go cra - zy is what I will do. ___ If I can't have you

I don't want — no - bo - dy, ba - by, if I can't have you. Ah, ____

____ Ah, ____ if I can't have you, I don't want ____

____ no - bo - dy, ba - by, if I can't have you. Ah, ____

D.%. al Coda ⊕ *CODA*

____ Ah. ____ Can't let
mp
ea - si - ly to you, my love, to

dreams that ne - ver will come true. ____ Am I strong e - nough to see it

D.%.%. and Fade

through? ____ Go cra - zy is what I will do. ____ If I can't have you.

TRAGEDY

Words & Music by Barry Gibb, Robin Gibb, Maurice Gibb

Suggested registration: synth
Rhythm: disco
Tempo: medium (♩ = 120)

INTRO.

VERSES

Here I lie, in a lost and lone - ly
Night and day, there's a burn - ing down in -

part of town.
side of me.

Held in time, in a
Burn - ing love, with a

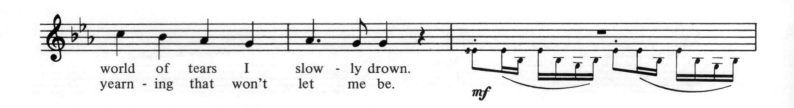

world of tears I slow - ly drown.
yearn - ing that won't let me be.

new hand position

Go - in' home, I just can't make it, all a - lone.
Down I go, I just can't take it, all a - lone.

I

real - ly should be hold - ing you, hold - ing you,

new hand position

mf cresc.

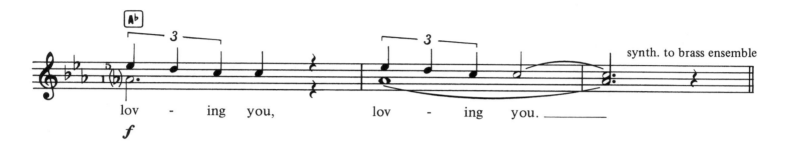

lov - ing you, lov - ing you. ___

f

synth. to brass ensemble

CHORUS

ff Tra - ge - dy, ___   *f* when the   feel - ing's gone, and you can't go   on,   it's

Tra - ge - dy, ___   when you   lose con - trol, and you got   no   soul, it's

ff tra - ge - dy. ___   *f* When the   morn - ing   cries, and you don't know why, it's

tra - ge - dy. ___   When the   morn - ing   cries, and you don't know why, it's

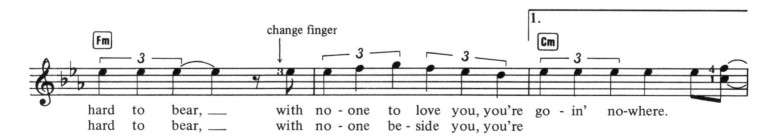

change finger

1.

hard   to   bear, ___   with no - one   to   love you, you're go - in' no-where.

hard   to   bear, ___   with no - one   be - side you, you're

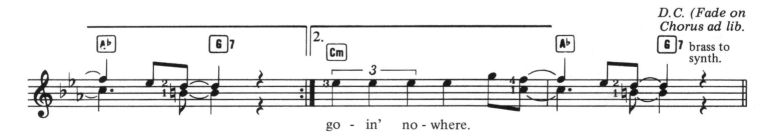

D.C. (Fade on
Chorus ad lib.

brass to
synth.

2.

go - in' no - where.

LOVE SO RIGHT

Words & Music by Barry Gibb, Robin Gibb & Maurice Gibb

Suggested registration: string ensemble
Rhythm: rock
Tempo: slow (♩ = 80)

She came on like the night, __ and she held on tight, __ and the

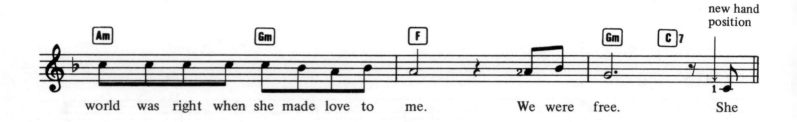

world was right when she made love to me. We were free. She

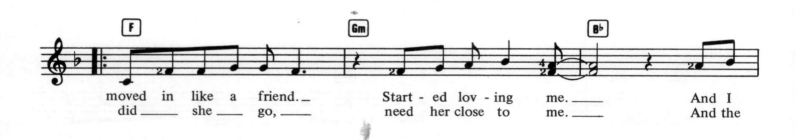

moved in like a friend. __ Start - ed lov - ing me. ___ And I
did ___ she ___ go, ___ need her close to me. ___ And the

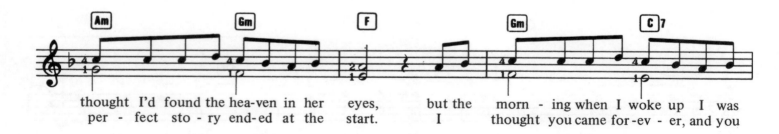

thought I'd found the hea-ven in her eyes, but the morn - ing when I woke up I was
per - fect sto - ry end-ed at the start. I thought you came for-ev - er, and you

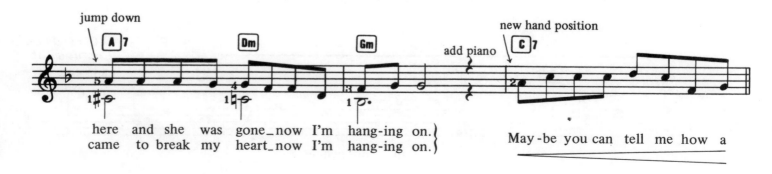

here and she was gone_ now I'm hang-ing on. }
came to break my heart_ now I'm hang-ing on. }

May-be you can tell me how a

CHORUS

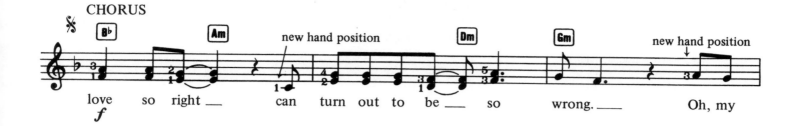

love so right __ can turn out to be __ so wrong. __ Oh, my

dar-ling. How __ a love so right __ can turn out to be __ so

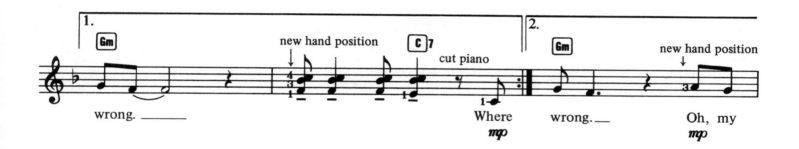

wrong. __ Where wrong. __ Oh, my

dar-ling I __ could take it in my stride, start liv-ing for the mo-ment.

May-be half the things we sought were ne-ver there. Sim-ply o-pen up your eyes, and

break it down to size. It is-n't real-ly fair. __ How a

TOO MUCH HEAVEN

Words & Music by Barry Gibb, Robin Gibb & Maurice Gibb

Suggested registration: flute
Rhythm: rock
Tempo: fairly slow (♩ = 84)

No-bo-dy gets__ too much hea-ven no more.__ It's much hard-er to come__ by, I'm
No-bo-dy gets__ too much love a-ny-more.__ It's as high as a moun-tain, and

wait-ing in line.___   hard-er to climb.___   You and me, girl, ___ got a
high-way to the sky. got a

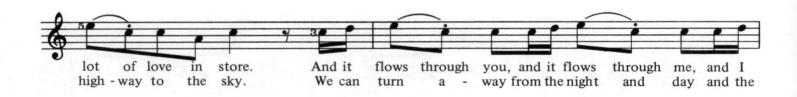

lot of love in store.   And it flows through you, and it flows through me, and I
high-way to the sky.   We can turn a - way from the night and day and the

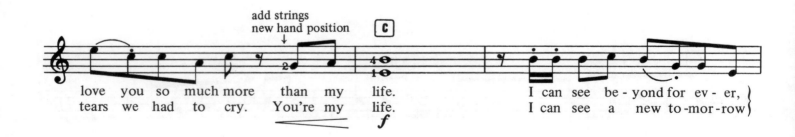

love you so much more than my life.   I can see be-yond for ev-er,
tears we had to cry. You're my life.   I can see a new to-mor-row

ev-'ry-thing we are will ne-ver die.   Lov-ing's such a beau-ti-ful thing.__

cut strings

new hand position

Oh, you make my world a
When you are to me the

mp

(D.C.)

sum - mer day. Are you just a dream, to fade a - way?
light a - bove, there for all to see, our pre - cious love.

No - bo - dy gets___ too much hea - ven no more,___ it's as high as a moun - tain, and

hard- er to climb.___ Oh _____

f

lov - ing's such a beau - ti - ful thing. _____ You make my world a

dim.

D.C. (Repeat first 4 bars and fade)

sum - mer day. Are you just a dream, to fade a - way?

mp

27

STAYIN' ALIVE

Words & Music by Barry Gibb, Robin Gibb & Maurice Gibb

Suggested registration: flute
Rhythm: disco
Tempo: medium (♩ = 104)

Well, you can tell by the way I use my walk, I'm a wo-man's man, no time to talk. With the

mu-sic loud and wo-men warm, I've been kicked a-round since I was born. And now it's

all right, it's O. K., and you may look the oth-er way. We can try to un-der-stand the

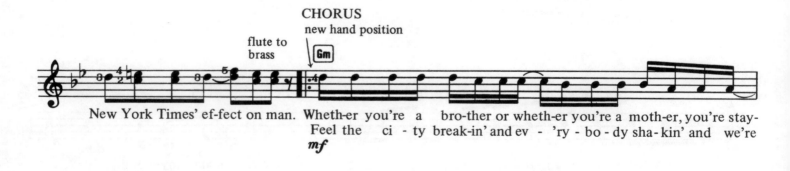

New York Times' ef-fect on man. Wheth-er you're a bro-ther or wheth-er you're a moth-er, you're stay-
Feel the ci - ty break-in' and ev - 'ry - bo - dy sha-kin' and we're

in' a - live, ___ stay-in' a - live. ___
stay - in' a - live, ___ stay-in' a - live. ___ Ah, ha, ha, ha,

stay-in' a-live,___ stay-in' a-live.___ Ah, ha, ha, ha,

stay-in' a-live.___

dim.

brass to flute

INTERLUDE

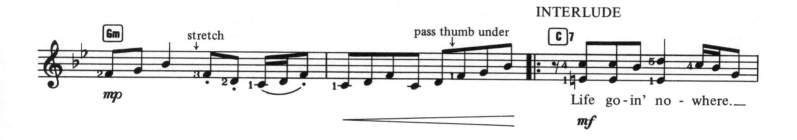

stretch

pass thumb under

Life go-in' no-where.___

mf

mp

squeeze together

Some-bo-dy help me.___ Some-bo-dy help me, yeah.___

mp

Life go-in' no-where.___ Some-bo-dy help me, yeah.___

mf

(Repeat and Fade)

jump down

Stay-in' a-live.

mp

RUN TO ME

Words & Music by Barry Gibb, Maurice Gibb & Robin Gibb

Suggested registration: saxophone
Rhythm: rock
Tempo: medim (♩ = 96)

If ev-er you've got rain in your heart,__
out in the cold,__

change finger   new hand position

some-one has hurt__ you, and torn you a-part.   Am I un-wise to
no-one be-side__ you, and no-one to hold.   Am I un-wise to

o-pen up your eyes to love me, and let it be like they
o-pen up your eyes to love me,   and when you've got

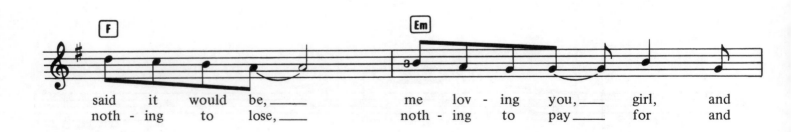

said it would be,__   me lov-ing you,__ girl,   and
noth-ing to lose,__   noth-ing to pay__ for   and

add piano

you lov-ing me.__ }
noth-ing to choose._ }   Am I un-wise to o-pen up your eyes to love

CHORUS

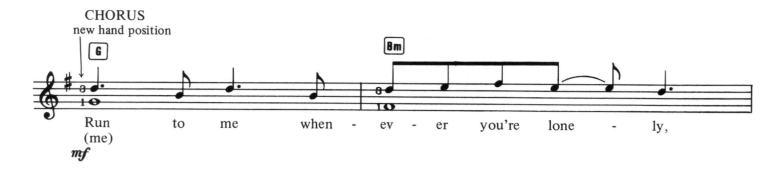

Run to me when-ev-er you're lone-ly,
(me)

run to me if you need a shoul-der. Now and then you'll

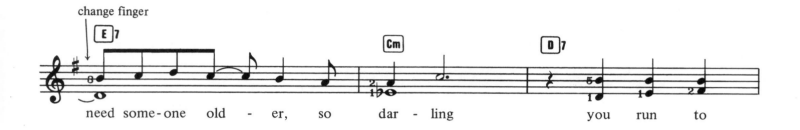

need some-one old-er, so dar-ling you run to

me. And when you're Run to me when-ev-er you're lone-ly,
(me.)

run to me if you need a should-er. Now and then you'll

need some one old-er, so dar-ling, you run to

YOU WIN AGAIN

Words & Music by Barry Gibb, Robin Gibb & Maurice Gibb

Suggested registration: piano
Rhythm: swing
Tempo: fast (♩ = 192)

There's no fight,__ you can't fight __ this bat - tle of love with__ me, __
life __ on earth,__ no oth - er could see me__ through, __

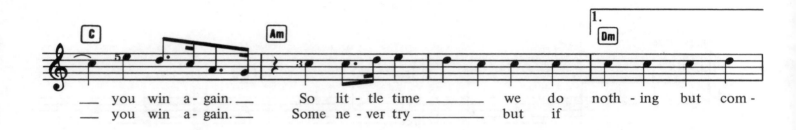

__ you win a - gain.__ So lit - tle time __ we do noth - ing but com -
__ you win a - gain. Some ne - ver try _____ but if

pete._____ There's no a - ny - bo - dy can, we can._____

BRIDGE

But I'll be,_____ I'll be_____ fol - low - ing

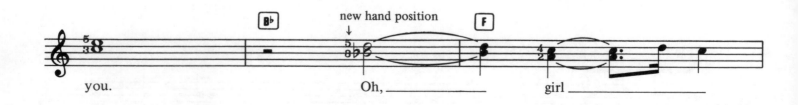

you. Oh,_____ girl_____

Oh ___ girl. Oh, ___

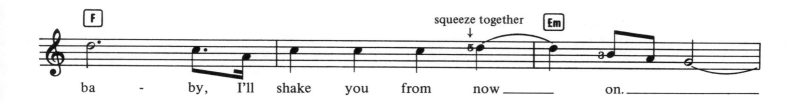

ba - by, I'll shake you from now ___ on. ___

___ I'm gon - na break down your de - fen - ces one by ___

___ one. ___ I'm gon - na hit you from all sides,

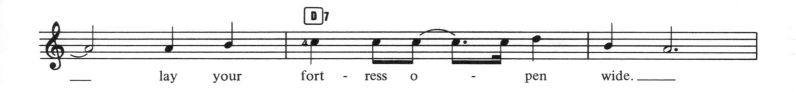

___ lay your fort - ress o - pen wide. ___

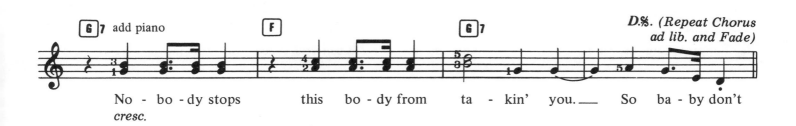

No - bo - dy stops this bo - dy from ta - kin' you. ___ So ba - by don't
cresc.

NIGHT FEVER

Words & Music by Barry Gibb, Robin Gibb & Maurice Gibb

Suggested registration: brass ensemble
Rhythm: disco
Tempo: medium (♩ = 108)

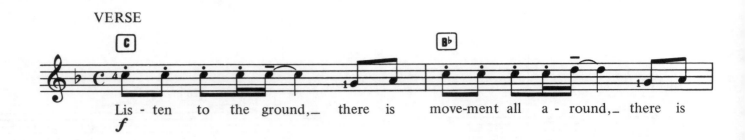

Lis - ten to the ground,_ there is move-ment all a - round,_ there is

some - thing go - in' down,_ and I can feel it. On the

waves of the air_ there is dan - cin' out there,_ if it's some-thin' we can share, we can

steal it. And that sweet ci - ty wo - man she moves through the light,_ con -

trol - ling my mind_ and my soul. ___ When you reach out for me ___ yeah! And the

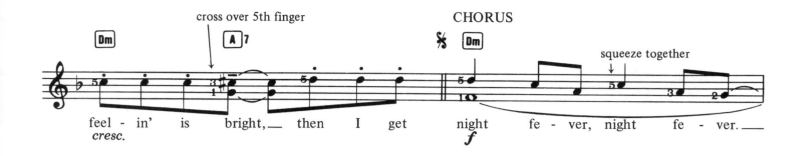

feel - in' is bright, then I get night fe - ver, night fe - ver.

cresc.

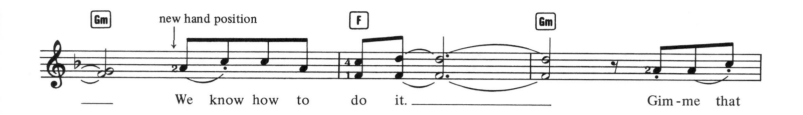

We know how to do it. Gim - me that

night fe - ver, night fe - ver. We know how to show it.

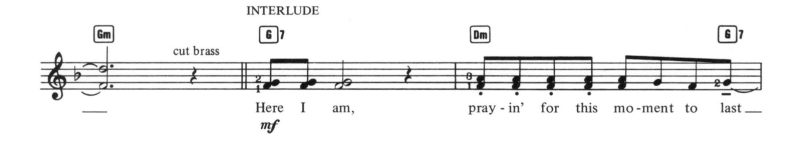

Here I am, pray - in' for this mo - ment to last

mf

liv - in' on the mu - sic so fine, borne on the wind,

cresc.

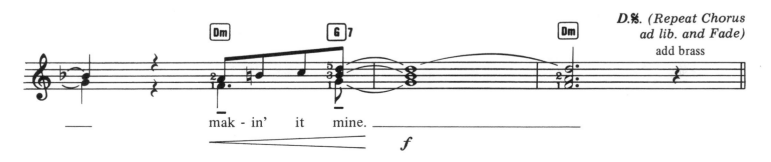

mak - in' it mine.

f

MORNING OF MY LIFE (IN THE MORNING)

Words & Music by Barry Gibb

Suggested registration: guitar
Rhythm: swing
Tempo: fairly fast (♩ = 132)

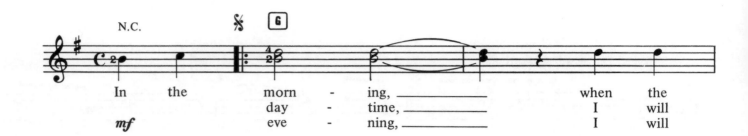

In the morn - ing, _____ when the
day - time, _____ I will
eve - ning, _____ I will

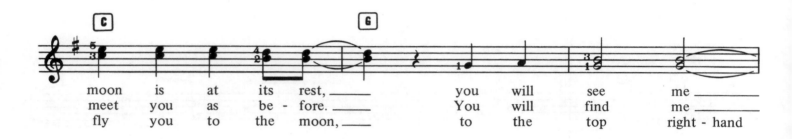

moon is at its rest, _____ you will see me _____
meet you as be - fore. _____ You will find me _____
fly you to the moon, _____ to the top right - hand

_____ at the time I love the best, _____ watch - ing
_____ wait - ing by the o - cean floor, _____ build - ing
cor - ner of the ceil - ing in my room, _____ where we'll

rain - bows _____ play on sun - light, _____
cas - tles _____ in the shift - ing sands, _____
stay _____ un - til the sun - shines _____

_____ pools of wa - ter, _____ iced from
_____ in a world that _____ no one
_____ an - oth - er day _____ to swing on

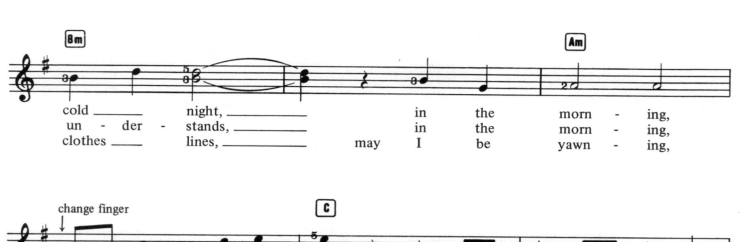

cold _____ night, _____ in the morn - ing,
un - der - stands, _____ in the morn - ing,
clothes _____ lines, _____ may I be yawn - ing,

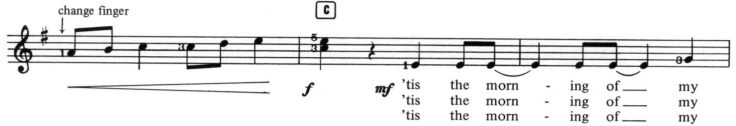

'tis the morn - ing of _____ my
'tis the morn - ing of _____ my
'tis the morn - ing of _____ my

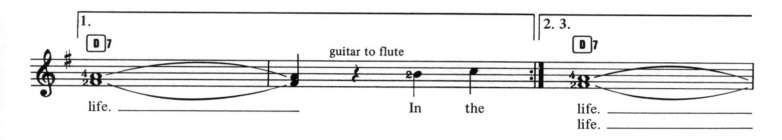

life. _____
In the life. _____
life. _____

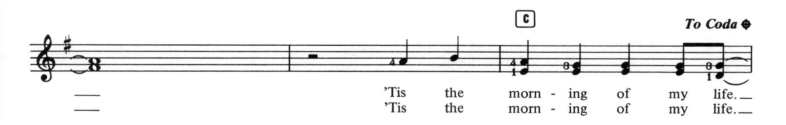

_____
'Tis the morn - ing of my life. _____
'Tis the morn - ing of my life. _____

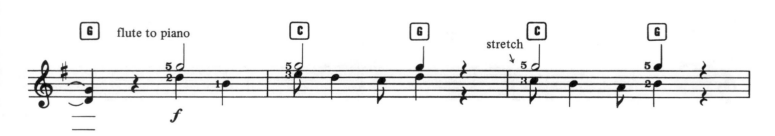

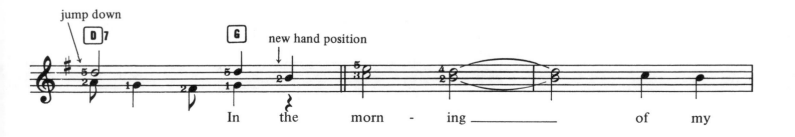

In the morn - ing _____ of my

life, _____ the min - utes take so

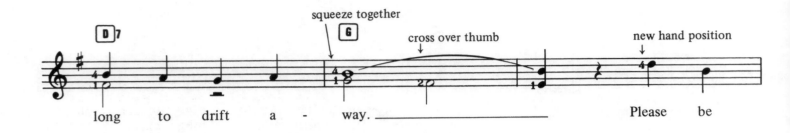

long to drift a - way. _____ Please be

pa - tient _____ with your life.

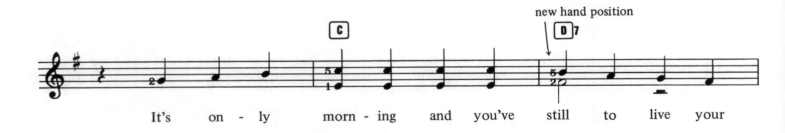

It's on - ly morn - ing and you've still to live your

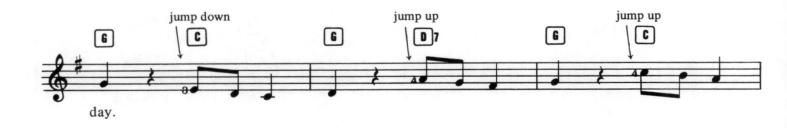

day.

In the

38

MASTER CHORD CHART

C
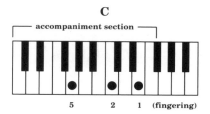
5   2   1   (fingering)

Cm
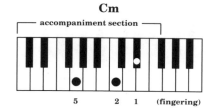
5   2   1   (fingering)

C7
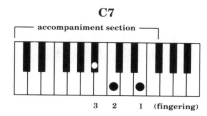
3   2   1   (fingering)

Db
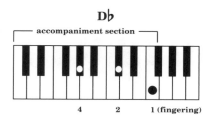
4   2   1 (fingering)

C♯m
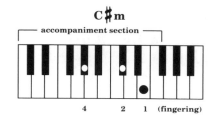
4   2   1   (fingering)

Db(C♯)7
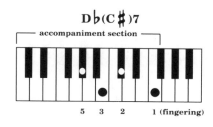
5   3   2   1 (fingering)

D
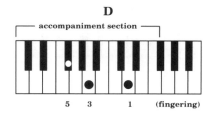
5   3   1   (fingering)

Dm
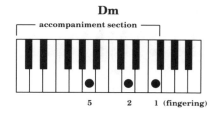
5   2   1 (fingering)

D7
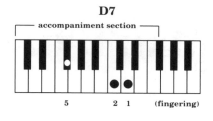
5   2 1   (fingering)

Eb
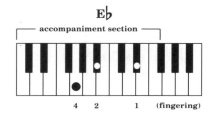
4   2   1   (fingering)

Ebm
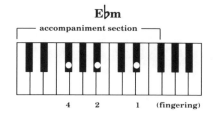
4   2   1   (fingering)

Eb7
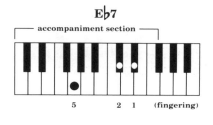
5   2 1   (fingering)

E
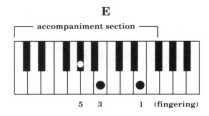
5   3   1   (fingering)

Em
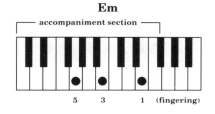
5   3   1   (fingering)

E7
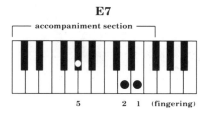
5   2 1   (fingering)

F
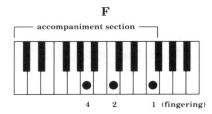
4   2   1 (fingering)

Fm
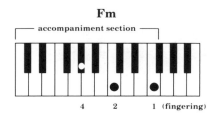
4   2   1   (fingering)

F7
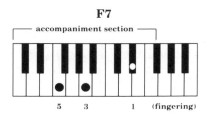
5   3   1   (fingering)

MASTER CHORD CHART

G♭(F♯)

accompaniment section

5   3   1   (fingering)

F♯m

accompaniment section

5   3   1   (fingering)

G♭(F♯)7

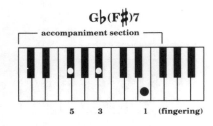

accompaniment section

5   3   1   (fingering)

G

accompaniment section

5   3   1   (fingering)

Gm

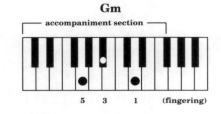

accompaniment section

5   3   1   (fingering)

G7

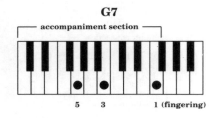

accompaniment section

5   3   1 (fingering)

A♭

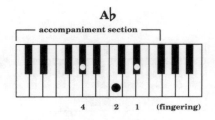

accompaniment section

4   2   1   (fingering)

A♭m

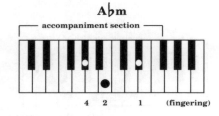

accompaniment section

4   2   1   (fingering)

A♭7

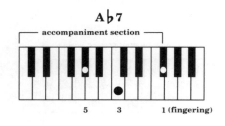

accompaniment section

5   3   1 (fingering)

A

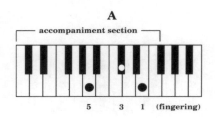

accompaniment section

5   3   1   (fingering)

Am

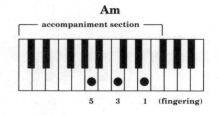

accompaniment section

5   3   1   (fingering)

A7

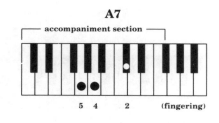

accompaniment section

5   4   2   (fingering)

B♭

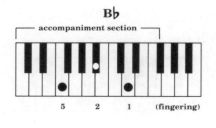

accompaniment section

5   2   1   (fingering)

B♭m

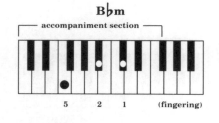

accompaniment section

5   2   1   (fingering)

B♭7

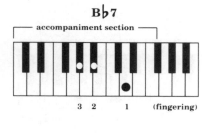

accompaniment section

3   2   1   (fingering)

B

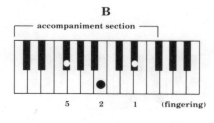

accompaniment section

5   2   1   (fingering)

Bm

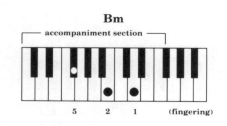

accompaniment section

5   2   1   (fingering)

B7

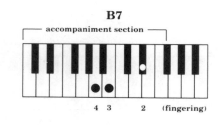

accompaniment section

4   3   2   (fingering)

8/02 (45018)